NASHVILLE, TENESSEE
MAY 7TH, 2023
9:45 P.M
IT'S THE SEVENTH STOP ON TAYLOR SWIFT'S RECORD-BREAKING "ERAS" TOUR.

SEVENTY THOUSAND PEOPLE HAVE SOLD OUT THIS ARENA SHOW, SOME SPENDING MORE THAN TWO MONTH'S RENT ON A TICKET TO SEE THEIR FAVORITE ARTIST PERFORM LIVE.
SEVERE
... BUT THE WEATHER HAS DIFFERENT PLANS FOR THEM.

STILL, THESE DIEHARD "SWIFTIES" REMAIN POSITIVE. DESPITE THUNDER, LIGHTNING, AND THE GENTLE URGING OF THEIR CITY'S LEADERSHIP TO TAKE THE NIGHT OFF... THEIR IDOL HAS YET TO OFFICIALLY CANCEL THE SHOW.
SO, WHILE THEIR HERO PLAYS A GAME OF CHICKEN WITH MOTHER NATURE HERSELF, THEY HUDDLE TOGETHER UNDER THE STADIUM'S MARQUEE AND SING THEIR FAVORITE TAYLOR SWIFT SONGS TO EACH OTHER TO PASS THE TIME.
♫♫ IT'S ME. HI! ♫♫

HOW LONG DO YOU THINK WE'RE GONNA HAVE TO WAIT?
MAYBE SHE MEANT IT LITERALLY WHEN SHE SANG "MEET ME AT MIDNIGHT". HAHAHA.
I DON'T CARE IF I HAVE TO WAIT EIGHT MORE HOURS. MY JOB WOULDN'T GIVE ME THE DAY OFF TO COME TO THE SHOW, SO I QUIT ON THE SPOT. I GOT NOTHING ELSE BETTER TO DO.

SHE WON'T LET US DOWN. I KNOW IT...

1:35AM

♫♫ LOOK WHAT YOU MADE ME DO... ♫♫
SURE, SOME OF THE SOFTER SWIFT-DEVOTEES INEVITABLY TURNED TAIL AND SOUGHT SHELTER FROM THE THUNDER AND LIGHTNING IN THE COMFORT OF THEIR LIGHTNING-PROOF HOMES (THE COWARDS).
BUT THE TRUE-BELIEVERS WHO WAITED FOR TAYLOR TO TAKE THE STAGE NEARLY FOUR HOURS LATER SWEAR THAT ONLY MADE THE ENVIRONMENT MORE ELECTRIC— BECAUSE THOSE WHO REMAINED WERE THE HARDEST OF THE HARDCORE, WHO KNEW EVERY WORD OF EVERY LYRIC BY HEART AND WEREN'T SHY ABOUT SINGING ALONG WITH THEIR FAVORITE ARTIST.

MAKE SOME NOISE FOR MY PHENOMENAL DANCERS WHO DANCED IN THE RAIN FOR YOU ALL NIGHT... THE FACT THAT YOU STAYED FOR US, THAT YOU GAVE US EVERYTHING YOU HAD — WE LOVE YOU SO MUCH, NASHVILLE. WE WILL NEVER FORGET THIS NIGHT.

YOU KNOW YOU COULD HAVE CALLED THE SHOW OFF, RIGHT? NOBODY WOULD HAVE GIVEN YOU GRIEF ABOUT NOT WANTING TO DROWN ONSTAGE.
I CAN'T THINK OF A BETTER WAY TO GO OUT.

BESIDES: IF YOU GIVE ME THE CHOICE BETWEEN DEATH-BY-LIGHTNING OR DISAPPOINTING A STADIUM FULL OF "SWIFTIES"... I'M TAKING THE LIGHTNING EVERY TIME.

YOU'RE A WORKAHOLIC.
NAH. I'M JUST GRATEFUL. WHEN I THINK ABOUT THIS CAREER MY SUPPORTERS HAVE GIVEN ME, WHAT ELSE COULD I BE?

AND WHAT A CAREER IT HAS BEEN.
TAYLOR SIGNED HER FIRST RECORDING CONTRACT AT AGE 14, IN 2006, WITH THE LABEL BIG MACHINE.
I CAN'T BELIEVE THIS IS HAPPENING!
TRUST ME, WE ARE EXCITED TO BE IN THE TAYLOR SWIFT BUSINESS.

SHE RELEASED HER FIRST RECORD, APPROPRIATELY TITLED TAYLOR SWIFT, LATER THAT YEAR.
NEW RE
IS THAT ONE ANY GOOD?
SURPRISINGLY, YEAH. MODERN COUNTRY ISN'T NORMALLY MY JAM, BUT THIS "TAYLOR SWIFT" GAL IS PRETTY SOLID.
HMM. ALRIGHT. I'LL GIVE IT A SHOT.

THE ALBUM'S THREE SINGLES, "TIM MCGRAW", "TEARDROPS ON MY GUITAR" AND "OUR SONG" VASTLY EXCEEDED BIG MACHINE'S EXPECTATIONS...
HOT DANG! THIS RECORD DOES KINDA RULE!

...RESULTING IN TAYLOR BECOMING THE FIRST FEMALE COUNTRY ARTIST IN HISTORY TO HAVE WRITTEN A PLATINUM-CERTIFIED ALBUM.

TAYLOR'S NEXT RECORD, FEARLESS, WAS HIGHLY ANTICIPATED BY FANS AND CRITICS ALIKE.

EMPOWERED BY THE SUCCESS OF HER FIRST ALBUM, TAYLOR TOOK SOME SERIOUS RISKS AS A WRITER. FEARLESS' BIG SINGLE, LOVE STORY, WASN'T AN AUTOBIOGRAPHICAL DIARY ENTRY SET TO MUSIC. IT, AND THE MUSIC VIDEO THAT ACCOMPANIED IT, WERE INSPIRED BY THE WORKS OF WILLIAM SHAKESPEARE.

WEEK OF JANUARY 17, 2009
THIS WEEK
1
Just Dance
Lady Gaga Featur
2
Single Lad
Beyonce
3
Live You
TI. Featuring R
4
Love Sto
Taylor Swift
...AND HER GAMBLE PAID OFF IN A BIG, BAD WAY. LOVE STORY LANDED IN THE TOP FIVE FOR BILLBOARD'S HOT 100 POP SONGS, AND STAYED THERE FOR SEVENTEEN WEEKS— A DOWNRIGHT MIRACULOUS FEAT FOR A COUNTRY TRACK.

TAYLOR'S NEXT ENTRY, SPEAK NOW, HEAVILY LEANED INTO HER MAINSTREAM APPEAL.

THE SINGLE YOU BELONG WITH ME IS AN UNABASHEDLY POP ANTHEM THAT SPEAKS TO A UNIVERSAL TEENAGE EXPERIENCE.
TAYLOR'S "CLARK KENT MEETS THE GIRL NEXT DOOR FROM A 90'S ROM COM" COSTUME FOR THE MUSIC VIDEO IS A SELF-AWARE, TONGUE-IN-CHEEK ACKNOWLEDGEMENT OF HOW POTENTIALLY CRINGE-WORTHY THE SONG'S ULTRA-EARNEST LYRICS CAN BE.
You OK?

HER FANS ATE IT UP. YOU BELONG WITH ME CEMENTS TAYLOR'S STATUS AS THE POST-IRONIC VOICE OF A HER GENERATION.
THE SONG BECOMES THE FIRST EVER TO REACH NUMBER ONE ON BOTH THE HOT COUNTRY SONGS AND ALL-GENRE CHARTS.
IT GOES PLATINUM SEVEN TIMES.

SWIFT MAKES ANOTHER MASSIVE CREATIVE RISK WITH HER NEXT RECORD, 2012'S RED...

HAVING BEEN PIGEONHOLED BY FANS AND CRITICS ALIKE AS THE "SWEET, AND PAINFULLY SINCERE GIRL-NEXT- DOOR", TAYLOR COMES OUT SWINGING WITH WE ARE NEVER EVER GETTING BACK TOGETHER.

THE TRACK IS EVERYTHING THAT SWIFT'S PREVIOUS ENTRIES HAVEN'T BEEN. IT'S ANGRY. IT'S ANGSTY. IT'S EDGY. IN FACT, THE CHORUS FEELS LIKE SOMETHING OUT OF A POP PUNK OFFERING.
WHAT IS THIS?
IT ALIENATES SOME FANS.
IS THAT REALLY TAYLOR? SHE SOUNDS SO...MAD!

BUT IT ATTRACTS MANY, MANY MORE.
HEY, HAVE YOU HEARD THE NEW TAYLOR SWIFT RECORD?
I KNOW! IT KINDA SLAPS, RIGHT?
TURNS OUT THE CHEERLEADER HAS AN EDGE TO HER.
APPARENTLY.

IN HER 2014 RECORD 1989, SWIFT LEANS INTO THE SLIGHTLY-MORE-CYNICAL TONE SHE ESTABLISHED IN HER PREVIOUS SINGLE.
IN HER REVIEW OF THE ALBUM FOR PITCHFORK, REVIEWER VRINDA JAGOTA WROTE: "SWIFT LOSES HER NAÏVETÉ, DONS A SENSE OF UNFAZED NONCHALANCE, AND LEARNS TO NAVIGATE A WORLD THAT UNDERAPPRECIATED HER LYRICISM AND SHAMED HER FOR DATING TOO MANY MEN... FOR THOSE WHO MIGHT OPENLY CRY WHILE LISTENING TO RED, THE FIRST LISTEN OF 1989 STINGS OF INDIFFERENCE."

IN HER VIDEO FOR SHAKE IT OFF, SHE DRESSES UP LIKE A LITERAL CHEERLEADER— POKING FUN AT THE MEDIA'S PERCEPTION OF HER:

HER NEXT SINGLE, BLANK SPACE, POKES FUN AT HER HATERS' COMMON GRIPE THAT SHE ALWAYS CASTS HERSELF AS A VICTIM IN HER BALLADS, AND ASSUMES THE PERSPECTIVE OF HER EXES FOR THE FIRST TIME...
THEY'LL TELL YOU I'M INSANE...

BUT 1989'S LAST HIT, BAD BLOOD, IS COMPLETELY DEVOID OF THE SELF-DEPRECATING COMMENTS THAT MADE THE LAST TWO SINGLES POP.
IT'S A "DON'T CENSORED WITH ME" WARNING, WHOSE RELATIVELY-AGGRESSIVE LYRICS ARE ACCOMPANIED BY AN OVER-THE-TOP MUSIC VIDEO THAT DEPICTS TAYLOR AS A GUN-TOTING ASSASSIN, FLANKED BY LITERALLY DOZENS OF HER MOST POPULAR AND POWERFUL FRIENDS.
THOSE NAMES INCLUDE...
ZENDAYA COLEMAN
GIGI HADID

MARTHA HUNT
SERAPH MCNEIL
ELLIE GOULDING
KARLIE KLOSS
JESSICA ALBA
LENA DUNHAM
CARA DELEVINGNE
SELENA GOMEZ
KENDRICK LAMAR
MARISKA HARGITAY
HAYLEY WILLIAMS
CINDY CRAWFORD
ELLEN POMPEO
LILY ALDRIDGE
HAILEE STEINFELD

BACKLASH FROM THE CREATIVE COMMUNITY COMES HARD AND...SWIFT. EVERYONE WHO HAD EVER DONE TAYLOR DIRTY TAKES BAD BLOOD'S LYRICS PERSONALLY, AND STARTS SPIRALING ON SOCIAL MEDIA AND ON INTERVIEWS TO REFRAME THE NARRATIVE AND MAKE TAYLOR OUT TO BE THE BAD GUY.

OH...
THIS INCLUDES EX-FRIEND KATY PERRY, WHO HAD A FALLING OUT WITH TAYLOR AFTER THE ATTEMPTED TO POACH SOME OF SWIFT'S BACKUP DANCERS OUT FROM UNDER HER.

AND KANYE WEST, WHO PUBLICLY— AND RUDELY— INTERRUPTED HER ACCEPTANCE SPEECH AT THE MTV VIDEO MUSIC AWARDS, TO SAY THAT HIS FRIEND BEYONCE DESERVED TAYLOR'S "VIDEO OF THE YEAR" AWARD OVER HER.
...CRAP.

AND KANYE'S THEN-WIFE KIM KARDASHIAN... WHO RELEASED EDITED TEXTS BETWEEN THE TWO TO THE MEDIA, IMPLYING THAT TAYLOR HAD GIVEN CONSENT TO KANYE FOR THE VARIOUS RUDE REMARKS HE HAD MADE ABOUT HER IN HIS SONGS OVER THE YEARS.
...

OVERNIGHT, THE PUBLIC'S PERCEPTION OF TAYLOR SHIFTS FROM INOFFENSIVE LITTLE INDUSTRY DARLING TO SCANDALOUS CENTER OF CONTROVERSY.
TAYLOR! HOW DO YOU RESPOND TO THE ALLEGATIONS THAT—
HAVE YOU SEEN THE ARTICLE THAT ALLEGES—
ON TWITTER—
AS ANY TRUE ARTIST WOULD DO, TAYLOR ALCHEMIZES THE EXPERIENCE INTO MATERIAL FOR A NEW RECORD.

A LOT OF FOLKS SPECULATED THAT SWIFT'S NEXT ALBUM WAS GOING TO BE AN APOLOGY OF SORTS, WALKING BACK THE OUT-OF-PLACE EDGINESS OF 1989 AND RETURNING TO THE "UNPROBLEMATIC" PERSONA THAT MADE HER POPULAR IN THE FIRST PLACE.
HERE LIES
TAYLOR SW
REPUTATION

...THEY WERE WRONG.

2017'S REPUTATION COMES OUT SWINGING WITH THE SINGLE LOOK WHAT YOU MADE ME DO, AN EASTER-EGG-FILLED SPECTACLE THAT— FOR TAYLOR'S ULTRA-ATTENTIVE FANS— DIRECTLY ADDRESSES THE VARIOUS RUMORS, SPATS, AND SCANDALS FOR THE PREVIOUS YEAR.

TAYLOR EXCLUDES HERSELF FROM MEDIA ATTENTION AFTER REPUTATION'S RELEASE, FORGOING THE NORMAL TELEVISION SHOW APPEARANCES AND MAGAZINE INTERVIEWS THAT GO HAND-IN-HAND WITH RELEASING A NEW WORK.

BUT SHE STILL SHOWS UP FOR THE FANS.
IN FACT, TAYLOR CREDITS THE REPUTATION STADIUM TOUR—WITH ITS OVERWHELMINGLY POSITIVE FAN INTERACTIONS— AS THE MAIN FACTOR IN HER RECOVERING MENTAL HEALTH.
WE LOVE YOU, TAYLOR!
I LOVE YOU GUYS TOO! THANK YOU FOR COMING OUT!

EMPOWERED AND EMBOLDENED BY THE EXPERIENCE, SHE COMMITS TO MAKING SEVERAL POSITIVE CHANGES TO BOTH HER LIFE, AND CAREER...

$$
IN 2019, TAYLOR SPLITS UP WITH HER LABEL BIG MACHINE, AND SIGNS TO REPUBLIC RECORDS.

LATER THAT YEAR, SHE RELEASES HER NEXT RECORD, LOVER— WHICH SWIFT DESCRIBES AS "A LOVE LETTER TO LOVE ITSELF."
TAYLOR TAKES ADVANTAGE OF HER NEWFOUND ARTISTIC FREEDOM, AND FILLS THE ALBUM WITH SONGS THAT RUN THE GAMUT FROM OLD-SCHOOL COUNTY...

...TO STRAIGHT-UP BUBBLEGUM POP.

AND SHE ALSO, FOR THE FIRST TIME IN HER CAREER, ADDRESSES THE AMERICAN POLITICAL CLIMATE, WITH THE SONG YOU NEED TO CALM DOWN, A GAY RIGHTS ANTHEM WHOSE MUSIC VIDEO INCLUDES CAMEOS FROM SUCH LGBTQIA+ LUMINARIES AS...
ELLEN DEGENERES
RUPAUL
LAVERNE COX

BILLY PORTER
AND THE CAST OF NETFLIX'S QUEER EYE.

POSSIBLY EVEN MORE IMPACTFUL THAN HER NEXT RECORD, IS MISS AMERICANA— THE SELF-PRODUCED DOCUMENTARY THAT FOLLOWED IT.
TAYLOR SWIFT
MISS AMERICANA
THE DOC FOLLOWS TAYLOR BEHIND-THE-SCENES, DOCUMENTING A SLEW OF SENSITIVE TOPICS THAT THE SINGER/ SONGWRITER HAD NEVER BEFORE OPENED UP ABOUT IN INTERVIEWS, INCLUDING: HER BATTLES WITH BODY DYSMORPHIA, HER MOTHER'S CANCER DIAGNOSIS, AND THE TOXICITY OF SO-CALLED "SOCIAL MEDIA".
OBVIOUSLY, ANYTIME YOU'RE STANDING UP AGAINST OR FOR ANYTHING, YOU'RE NEVER GOING TO RECEIVE UNANIMOUS PRAISE...

"...BUT THAT'S WHAT FORCES YOU TO BE BRAVE. AND THAT'S WHAT'S DIFFERENT ABOUT THE WAY I LIVE MY LIFE NOW."
WOW...
THIS HELPS TO SHED HER "COOKIE CUTTER POP-STAR" IMAGE, AND ATTRACTS A LEGION OF NEW FANS WHO ARE DRAWN TO HER AUTHENTICITY AND RELATABILITY.

SHE PUT OUT AN ASTONISHING TWO RECORDS IN 2020. FOLKLORE FEELS LIKE AN IINDIE FOLK RECORD.

AND EVERMORE WHICH HAS A MORE ALTERNATIVE FLAVOR.

AN EXTREME PUBLIC DISPUTE WITH BIG MACHINE, THE FIRST COMPANY SHE EVER HAD A RECORDING CONTRACT WITH, LEADS TO HER RE-RECORDING AND RE-RELEASING ALL OF HER EARLIEST SONGS.
THE RE-RECORDED SINGLE "ALL TOO WELL (10 MINUTE VERSION)" FROM THE RECORD RED (TAYLOR'S VERSION) BECOMES THE LONGEST SONG IN HISTORY TO TOP THE HOT 100 LIST— PROVING ONCE-AND-FOR-ALL THE DEDICATION OF HER LOYAL FANBASE.
All Too Well
Taylor Swift (10:00)

THE PRESENT:
IN AN ERA DEFINED BY ITS OBSESSION WITH LABELS AND CULTURAL ECHO-CHAMBERS, TAYLOR SWIFT IS A LIVING REMINDER THAT AUTHENTICITY AND ARTISTRY CAN CUT THROUGH ALL THE NOISE AND REACH PEOPLE FROM EVERY WALK OF LIFE.

Eric M. Esquivel — Writer

Ramon Salas — Art

Benjamin Glibert — Letters

Darren G. Davis — Editor

Ramon Salas — Cover

Cover B: Yonami

Darren G. Davis
Publisher

Maggie Jessup
Publicity

Susan Ferris
Entertainment Manager

Steven Diggs Jr.
Marketing Manager

Printed in the USA
CPSIA information can be obtained
at www.ICGtesting.com
LVHW081745181223
766780LV00007B/213